"May you walk gently through the ...
and know its beauty."

NATIVE APACHE PEOPLE BLESSING

ISBN: 9781916046115
Story copyright © Jo Earlam
Illustrations copyright © Mark Hannon

First published October 2020

Rosa's Footprint

Jo Earlam   *M Hannon*

Written by Jo Earlam

Illustrations by Mark Hannon

Published by Turtletastic Titles

JO EARLAM
Author

Jo began a journalistic career on the Sidmouth Herald in 1986 and has lived in the area ever since. This story is inspired by her passion for the outdoors, enjoyment of the spectacular East Devon coastline and countryside, and concern for the impact of humanity's collective footprint on the natural world. Walking on Dartmoor as a child with her dad Bernard, they'd discuss why people left rubbish in beautiful places. And when she was tired, he did say to put her foot where his had been.

MARK HANNON
Artist/Illustrator & Designer

Westcountry born and bred, Mark Hannon has been involved in
Art and Design throughout his life... from his roots in primary school comics, secondary school influences from his Art Teacher father, through to an Honours degree in Scientific and Technical Graphics, broadcast TV graphics, commercial illustration, print design and fine Art. His style of work and list of clients are as varied as his subject matter and his chosen media...ranging from cartoon, digital painting, watercolour, charcoal, pen and ink, acrylic and oils.
www.markhannon.co.uk

Jo and Mark's two previous books:

Tuamor the Turtle
A story about a Pacific Ocean turtle and marine plastic pollution.
Published November 2015
www.tuamortheturtle.com

Archie Space Dog
A tribute to the many small dogs sent into space, as part of mankind's bid to reach the moon.
Published May 2019
www.archiespacedog.wordpress.com

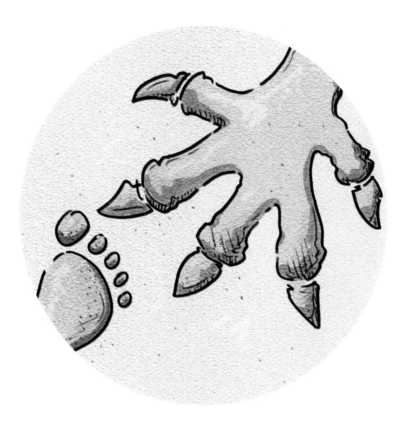

Foreword

You never know what you might find on a beach.
Seashells, pretty pebbles, driftwood, or just rubbish
that other people have left behind.
But maybe, like Colin in this book, you will find
something much more unusual, something that has
an amazing story to tell from long, long ago.
So, it is well worth keeping your eyes open when you
are on the beach, but remember not to go too near to
cliffs, and at the end of your visit leave just footprints!

Dr Rob Coram, palaeontologist,
who found the footprint

Present day

Sidmouth, below Peak Hill

It was a bright, sunny morning as Colin jumped off his paddle board into the water.

He stepped barefoot on to the rocks, standing alone and feeling small beneath the big red cliffs.

Cliffs with beautiful views that stretched for miles.

This spot was far from the main beach and not many people came here.

Then Colin saw something unusual.

Something that grabbed his attention.

240 million years earlier
When Sidmouth was part of central Pangea

Rosa the rauisuchian trudged along the path of hot, bumpy pebbles and thick mud. Her father Reggie was far ahead, lumbering crocodile-like on all fours. "I'm tired Daddy," Rosa cried.

"Wait for me."

Insects buzzed in Rosa's eyes and large shiny dragonflies flew overhead.

The sunshine was bright, and the few tall trees gave little shade.

In the distance, hills
shimmered in the haze.
The pools and streams
where water should have been
were dry.

There was nothing to eat
and nothing to drink
in this land-locked,
desert-like place.

Rosa slumped down and wailed:
"I can't go any further Daddy."

"I'm hungry and thirsty."

Reggie paused, standing upright on his back legs.

A huge, scaly-backed,
scary-looking monster of a reptile.

Walking on two feet, he returned to Rosa and stood swishing
his long tail, towering above his little daughter, razor-sharp
white teeth glinting as he opened his wide mouth.

Looking down, he said in a kind gentle voice:
"Rosa we need to find water and food.
I know you're tired, but we must keep going."

"But why isn't there anything to eat or drink?"
Rosa demanded crossly.

"Because others have been here before and
taken all there is," said Reggie.

"They've stripped everything bare."

Rosa looked at the mud around her. It was churned up by hundreds of different feet of all shapes and sizes, claws, toes, paws, and talons. Scattered around were half-chewed bones of smaller creatures and remains of plants and tree branches that had been trampled upon.

"Gosh! It looks as if someone's had a party, made a big mess and left nothing for anyone else," Rosa said.

"It's horrible. I wish you'd never brought me here."

With that she began to cry.
"Rosa, I'm sorry" said her father.

"Please don't get upset."

"This is meant to be an
adventure!"

Rosa cried even more loudly.

"Oh dear," said Reggie. The walk wasn't turning out as planned. He was taking Rosa to a favourite spot his grandfather used to take him as a boy. But with years of little water and hot sun, much of the land around had dried out.

Reggie spotted a pebble in a shape that could be rolled along the ground. He decided to try and cheer his little daughter up.

"Hey Rosa," he said. "I remember grandad playing this game with me, Foot Pebble."

"You have to put your foot against the pebble and push it like this."

He gently edged the rounded stone towards Rosa.

"Come on, have a go!"

Rosa looked sulky. "No! I'm not playing," she said.
"Come on," said Reggie. "Just one little kick.
See if you can aim it straight back to me."

Rosa sighed, but to please her father she kicked the pebble
and it did easily roll straight to him.

"Nice pass," said Reggie. "And again!"

They carried on their walk, happily playing until Rosa grew tired.
"Are we there yet?" she asked. "Just a bit further," said Reggie.

"I know you're struggling. Put your feet where mine have been.
It will help you keep up with me."

As Rosa put her little clawed toes inside her father's footprints, she thought with each step about the marks they were leaving in the earth.

They came eventually to the top of a hill, with a stunning view. You could see for miles.

"Wow, this is amazing Daddy.
Now I know why you brought me."

"It's beautiful."

"It's one of the few spots around here that remain unspoilt," said her father.

"Not many come this far, so the plants don't get eaten and destroyed, no mess is left behind, and the land is able to cope with the impact of those that do walk here."

Rosa looked around.

The trees still had leaves, giving shade from the sun. Patches of ferns grew alongside small clean pools of water.

She thought about the impact every creature has upon
the world, and how all living things and all growing
things rely on each other.

She thought about the footprints she and her father
had left on the walk, the thousands of feet that might
one day find their way here.

"I don't want to be someone who leaves a big mess,
spoils a place like this," she blurted out.

"Rosa, my love, of course you won't be!" said Reggie.
"I know you'd never be like that."

"That's why I wanted you to see this wider view
and be inspired by it like I was."

"It's a wonderful world, and I know you'll walk
lightly through it."

"Come on, let's rest and enjoy the peace of this moment."

Reggie sat down and began to snooze, his eyes closing, but Rosa's attention was caught by a green shoot sprouting from the ground. It had delicate leaves on a single woody stem.

It stood boldly upright reaching for the sun but so fragile it would be crushed by careless feet.

It was a perfect but tiny young tree.

Rosa felt strangely protective,
wanting to help this
little twiggy plant grow.

If it was given a chance to get bigger,
it would become tall and strong,
provide shade and feed
hungry mouths in the future.

She wondered how she might
keep it safe, alert others
to take extra care.

She thought of the footprints
she and her father had left,
the attention she'd given to
each step, treading
carefully behind him.

Reggie woke from his nap, to see Rosa
carefully pushing her feet deliberately into
the mud, leaving a clear trail of deep claw marks.

"Rosa my love, what are you doing?" he asked.

"It's a signed path Daddy, leaving space for
the little green shoots to grow.
It asks everyone to walk gently through this
special place."

"It's a message
to think footprint!"

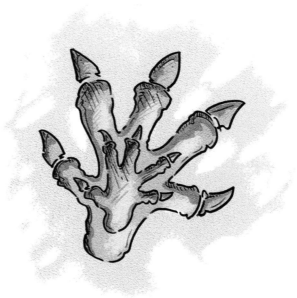

Back to present day
Sidmouth

Colin gazed down with dismay. How could anyone be so careless in such a lovely spot. Scattered around were half-chewed bones, the remains of a barbecue, plastic wrappers, cutlery and plates.

He began packing everything into a bag. In the distance he saw a plastic ball, being blown by the wind towards the sea.

He hurried to stop it reaching the water.

As he got closer, he saw that bottles and cans had been mixed with pebbles to make goal posts, for beach football.

"What a mess," he said, sorting through the pile, his hand touching the solid red sandstone rock beneath.

He knew the beach was part of the Jurassic Coast, a land roamed by prehistoric beasts and dinosaurs millions of years earlier.

Colin pushed the last pebble away feeling a shiver of excitement as his fingers traced around…one, two, three, four, five… matching marks set deep within the sandstone.

Distinctive toes that ended in sharp claws.

"Wow!" said Colin.

"A footprint."

What creature had walked where he was now?
What had it been like? A living, breathing animal,
leaving just this trace upon the earth, a single sign of its presence.

Colin stood for a moment
in silence and awe.

Then,
lifting the bag of rubbish
with a sigh,
he walked away,
deep in thought.

This story was inspired by a real trace fossil footprint, found on the
beach below Peak Hill, Sidmouth, in the winter of 2012/13
by a palaeontologist from Bristol University, Dr Robert Coram.

Dr Coram identified it as dating from 240 million years ago, left by
a rauisuchian, a pre-dinosaur age carnivorous reptile. It was the first
footprint of its kind to be found in this area. Dr Coram donated it to
Sidmouth Museum where the footprint is on display in the fossil
room.

The character of Colin was inspired by local artist Colin Bentley,
whose paintings of the Jurassic Coast illustrate how amazing and
special these cliffs are. Colin's website is www.colinbentley.com

THE FOOTPRINT

Sidmouth Museum is run by the Sid Vale Association, the oldest civic society in Britain.

Discover Sidmouth's fascinating history, people and places

www.sidmouthmuseum.co.uk

The footprint on display in the museum

The footprint being 3D scanned at FabLab Devon, Exeter Library

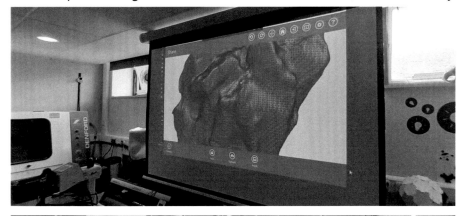

For information about scanning and engagement with schools
email: fablab@librariesunlimited.org.uk

THEO'S FOSSIL-TASTIC FACTS
Theo Woodcock, Age 10

Rauisuchian (raa-soo-shi-an)
Rauisuchians were a group of reptiles closely related to modern day crocodiles living in the Triassic period (251-199 million years ago). The largest species of rauisuchian could grow to the length of a school bus, that's big! They lived all over the world except Antarctica.
They usually walked on all fours but could rear up on their hind legs. These carnivores (meat eaters) had jaws full of huge curved teeth which they used to eat smaller herbivorous (plant eating) reptiles. Dinosaurs took over the earth and rauisuchians became extinct about 200 million years ago.

Pangea
Pangea was a big supercontinent which split into the continents we know today (Asia, Africa, North and South America, Europe, Antarctica and Australia). It existed 335-175 million years ago, because it was so big it would have been very hot in some places and very cold in other places.

Plants and trees
The biggest difference between Pangea and today is grass had not evolved yet, so no grass. There were not many trees except conifers and ferns but you did get horsetails and mosses in the Triassic.

Palaeontologist
A palaeontologist is a scientist who studies ancient fossils of plant and animal life and fossilised poo (coprolite).

Jurassic Coast
The Jurassic Coast is a stretch of coast that dates back to dinosaur times and has a lot of fossils in it. It stretches along the south coast of England from Exmouth to near Swanage. It possesses 185 million years of geological history. That's the study of what the earth is made from, like rocks, fossils and minerals.

How Sidmouth evolved from Pangea
England and Europe were an ancient part of Pangea so Sidmouth is no exception. As magma (lava before it hits the surface) levels rose under the surface of the earth, Pangea split apart along the continental plates. The UK is on the European plate. Later on, Britain and mainland Europe were connected by a chalk land bridge. When the water froze during the ice age this created a huge glacier (frozen river) stretching from between England and France to Norway. When this glacier melted the water caused erosion (water wearing down land). Because the land was made of chalk it eroded quickly until a huge slab of chalk fell off causing the sea level to rise and flooding the land.

How the footprint became a fossil, how it came to be found
When the rauisuchian stepped in something soft enough to leave a footprint but hard enough not to be washed away it left a footprint. Because of the pressure of sediment building up on top of it over time, it becomes rock. Erosion then wears away the sediment on top of it and the footprint is uncovered.

BERTIE'S BIG FOOTPRINT BEATERS

Bertie Dolphin, Age 9
(with help from his mum Dr Emma Pilgrim, an ecologist)

Hello, I'm Bertie. My mum says you only care for something that is special to you. I care about animals of all shapes and sizes. I am now vegetarian because I don't like them being killed for my food.

These are my tips for helping them.

Be Curious

We are out a lot walking our dog, along the beach, in woods, on the moor or along rivers. I am always finding something in rockpools, on wooden logs or on the ground. I have found fossils and lots of different beetles including the mighty minotaur, bloody nose and one of the rare oil beetles.

Be Creative

It can rain a lot in Devon, but there are times of the year when there isn't enough water. To help, I save water in plastic bottles and give it to our plants to drink.

I like giving things a new life by reusing:
Old loo rolls as building blocks for my pet gerbils or to grow beans and peas in.
Old ice cream sticks as plant labels for the vegetable seeds we grow.
Ceramic pots from shop-bought puddings or meals as water bowls for my pets.
Sowing seeds I have collected such as from acorns, beans and wheat, to see if they will grow.

Be Active

I like saving wild animals. I have rescued one of my favourite birds, a pigeon chick, an injured wood mouse and lots of different insects. I really like snails so please look at the ground, when you are walking, to make sure you don't step on them.

By sorting the weekly recycling I find new objects for reusing, like cardboard tubes which can be made into a mediaeval horn.

I like cycling and this is more environmentally friendly than always going by car.

Finally, I have helped Sidmouth Plastic Warriors clean rubbish from the beach.

I hope you will be inspired to create your own **Big Footprint Beaters** for things that are important to you.

FURTHER INFORMATION

Sidmouth Science Festival

Exciting scientific curiosity in all ages and abilities

www.sidmouthsciencefestival.org

Sidmouth Town Council

Managing local authority issues within Sidmouth, website links to other local organisations

www.sidmouth.gov.uk

Jurassic Coast Trust

Helping protect and conserve England's natural World Heritage Site

www.jurassiccoast.org

Seaton Jurassic

Interpretation centre engaging people with East Devon's unique geological, coastal and marine heritage

www.seatonjurassic.org

The Pebblebed Heaths Conservation Trust

Connecting people with the Pebblebed Heaths, Otter Estuary and important local habitats

www.pebblebedheaths.org.uk/education-outreach

British Geological Society

Information and learning resources for teachers, parents and students from primary school through to university

www.geolsoc.org.uk/education

Met Office

Online resources and education outreach about weather and climate change

www.metoffice.gov.uk/weather/learn-about/met-office-for-schools

AUTHOR THANKS

With thanks to all contributors to this book, especially Rob Coram
whose discovery of the footprint inspired this story and the community engagement
environmental awareness project TH!NK FOOTPRINT.

www.thinkfootprint.org
www.facebook.com/thinkfootprint

The project includes a writing competition for
children from local primary schools,
launched at Sidmouth Science Festival 2020.
Thanks to festival organisers and to the
Word Forest Organisation for assisting in
judging the children's writing competition.

The Word Forest Organisation is a small
environmental charity based in Lyme Regis,
dedicated to planting trees and making
our planet well again.
Plant a tree with them:
www.WordForest.org

What footprint will you leave?

HAVE A THINK!